# My Baby
### Record Book

Published by Hinkler Books Pty Ltd
45–55 Fairchild Street
Heatherton Victoria 3202 Australia
www.hinkler.com.au

hinkler

Text and design © Hinkler Books Pty Ltd 2004, 2010, 2012, 2014

Author: Kate Cody
Cover design: Hinkler Design Studio
Design: Sonia Dixon

ISBN: 978 1 7436 3676 3

Printed and bound in China

# My Baby

## Record Book

# Your Baby Girl's Birth

Name

...................................................................................................................

Date of birth

...................................................

Place of birth

...................................................

...................................................

...................................................

Day of the week

...................................................

Time of birth

...................................................

Birth weight

...................................................

Birth length

...................................................

Head circumference

...................................................

Delivered by

...................................................

Name of doctor

...................................................

Name of midwife

...................................................

About the birth

...................................................

...................................................

...................................................

...................................................

...................................................

Baby looks like

...................................................

...................................................

...................................................

...................................................

Baby's eyes are

...................................................

Baby's hair is

...................................................

Baby girl's star sign

...................................................

Visitors

....................................................

....................................................

....................................................

....................................................

....................................................

....................................................

Cards, flowers and presents

....................................................

....................................................

....................................................

....................................................

....................................................

....................................................

Memorable moments

....................................................

....................................................

....................................................

....................................................

....................................................

*One for luck, two for joy,*
*Three for a girl, four for a boy.*

Baby girl's birth photo

# Early Days at Home

Visitors

.............................................................

.............................................................

.............................................................

.............................................................

Cards, flowers and presents

.............................................................

.............................................................

.............................................................

.............................................................

.............................................................

## Feeding Routine
Duration of feed

.............................................................

Description of feed

.............................................................

.............................................................

.............................................................

Memorable moments

.............................................................

.............................................................

.............................................................

.............................................................

.............................................................

## Sleeping Routine
Sleeping times

.............................................................

.............................................................

Waking times

.............................................................

.............................................................

Newspaper birth announcement

6

Memorable moments

.................................................

.................................................

.................................................

## Welcome to the World

Our country's leader

.................................................

News headlines

.................................................

.................................................

Cost of a loaf of bread

.................................................

Cost of a stamp

.................................................

Cost of a newspaper

.................................................

Memorable moments

.................................................

.................................................

.................................................

Birth announcement card

*Higgledy piggledy my little hen,*
*She lays eggs for gentlemen.*
*Sometimes nine and sometimes ten,*
*Higgledy piggledy my little hen.*

# Naming Your Baby Girl

Baby girl's name

........................................

........................................

Reason for choosing name

........................................

........................................

Other names considered

........................................

........................................

........................................

........................................

Nicknames

........................................

........................................

## Naming Ceremony

Date

........................................

Place

........................................

Baby girl's outfit

........................................

........................................

Godparents

........................................

........................................

........................................

Naming day photo

Description of naming ceremony
and celebration

Cards and presents

How baby behaved

..............................................

..............................................

..............................................

..............................................

..............................................

Who was there

..............................................

..............................................

..............................................

..............................................

..............................................

..............................................

..............................................

..............................................

..............................................

..............................................

..............................................

..............................................

*Two little dickey-birds
sitting on a wall,
One named Peter,
One named Paul.
Fly away Peter,
Fly away Paul.
Come back Peter!
Come back Paul!*

9

# Baby Girl's Family Tree

## Baby Girl's Family

Mother's birth date

........................................

Father's birth date

........................................

Mother's place of birth

........................................

........................................

Father's place of birth

........................................

........................................

Significant family dates

........................................

Mother's life story in a nutshell

........................................

........................................

........................................

........................................

........................................

........................................

........................................

........................................

........................................

Father's life story in a nutshell

........................................

........................................

........................................

........................................

........................................

........................................

........................................

........................................

........................................

........................................

........................................

........................................

Brothers and sisters

........................................

........................................

........................................

........................................

Ages of brothers and sisters

........................................

........................................

........................................

........................................

| great grandmother | great grandfather | great grandmother | great grandfather | great grandmother | great grandfather | great grandmother | great grandfather |
|---|---|---|---|---|---|---|---|
| ................... | ................... | ................... | ................... | ................... | ................... | ................... | ................... |
| ................... | ................... | ................... | ................... | ................... | ................... | ................... | ................... |

grandmother

....................................

grandfather

....................................

grandmother

....................................

grandfather

....................................

mother

....................................

father

....................................

baby

....................................

# Sleepy Nights

Description of baby's nursery

.................................................

.................................................

.................................................

Description of the cot/crib

.................................................

.................................................

.................................................

First slept in cot/crib

.................................................

.................................................

First slept in own room

.................................................

.................................................

First slept through the night

.................................................

.................................................

Memorable moments

.................................................

.................................................

*Little Boy Blue*
*Come blow your horn,*
*The sheep's in the meadow*
*The cow's in the corn.*
*Where is the boy*
*Who looks after the sheep?*
*He's under the haystack*
*Fast asleep!*

## Helping Your Baby Girl to Sleep

Going to bed routine at night

...................................................

...................................................

...................................................

Lullabies that baby loves

...................................................

...................................................

...................................................

Bedtime stories that baby loves

...................................................

...................................................

...................................................

Bedtime toys or comforters

...................................................

...................................................

Settling techniques tried

...................................................

...................................................

Baby asleep

Most successful settling technique

...................................................

...................................................

...................................................

...................................................

...................................................

# Food to Grow

## Food and Drink Firsts

First began eating puréed food

..............................................

..............................................

First began eating mashed food

..............................................

..............................................

..............................................

First began eating solid food

..............................................

..............................................

Foods that baby loves

..............................................

..............................................

First drank from a spout cup

..............................................

..............................................

First drank through a straw

..............................................

..............................................

First drank from a cup

..............................................

..............................................

First sat in a high chair

..............................................

..............................................

..............................................

First ate with a spoon

..............................................

..............................................

First began sharing the family meal

..............................................

..............................................

Known food sensitivities

..............................................

..............................................

..............................................

..............................................

Memorable moments

..............................................

..............................................

..............................................

..............................................

..............................................

Baby eating

Pat a cake, pat a cake, baker's man,

Bake me a cake as fast as you can.

Pat it and prick it and mark it with B,

And put it in the oven for baby and me.

15

# Developmental Milestones

Began following with eyes

...........................................

...........................................

Began turning head to sound

...........................................

...........................................

First smiled

...........................................

...........................................

Began grasping rattle or soft toy

...........................................

...........................................

Began putting rattle or toy to mouth

...........................................

...........................................

First cooed

...........................................

...........................................

First held up head

...........................................

...........................................

First rolled over

...........................................

...........................................

Growing baby

Began to sit alone

....................................................

....................................................

First crawled

....................................................

....................................................

First stands with support

....................................................

....................................................

Began to walk with support

....................................................

....................................................

Started babbling

....................................................

....................................................

First words

....................................................

....................................................

....................................................

Started taking steps

....................................................

....................................................

Walked alone

....................................................

....................................................

First tooth

....................................................

....................................................

Sally go round the sun,
Sally go round the moon,
Sally go round the chimney pots,
On a Sunday afternoon.

# Things Baby Loves

Comforter

...........................................................

...........................................................

...........................................................

...........................................................

Things around home

...........................................................

...........................................................

...........................................................

...........................................................

Soft toys

...........................................................

...........................................................

...........................................................

Toys

...........................................................

Books

...........................................................

...........................................................

...........................................................

...........................................................

Nursery rhymes

...........................................................

...........................................................

...........................................................

...........................................................

Lullabies

...........................................................

...........................................................

...........................................................

...........................................................

Animals or pets

...........................................................

...........................................................

...........................................................

Games

...........................................................

...........................................................

...........................................................

...........................................................

Activities

..............................................

..............................................

..............................................

..............................................

..............................................

People

..............................................

..............................................

..............................................

..............................................

..............................................

Places

..............................................

..............................................

..............................................

..............................................

..............................................

This is the way the ladies ride,
Nimble, nimble, nimble, nimble;
This is the way the gentlemen ride,
A gallop, a trot, a gallop, a trot;
This is the way the farmers ride,
Jiggety-jog, jiggety-jog;
This is the way the farmboys ride,
Hobbledy-hoy, hobbledy-hoy;
This is the way the huntsmen ride,
A gallop, a gallop,
And down in the ditch!

# Fun with Water

## Bath-time

First bath

..................................................

First time in a big bath

..................................................

..................................................

Began sharing a bath

..................................................

..................................................

..................................................

Bath toys

..................................................

..................................................

Bath games

..................................................

..................................................

## Water Play

First trip to the beach or lake

..................................................

First water play in garden

..................................................

..................................................

Rub-a-dub dub,
Three men in a tub,
And who do you think they be?
A butcher, a baker,
A candle-stick maker,
Turn them out,
Knaves all three!

First splash in paddling pool

..................................................

..................................................

First dip in swimming pool

..................................................

..................................................

First swimming class

..................................................

..................................................

..................................................

..................................................

Your baby girl's swimming costume

..................................................

..................................................

..................................................

..................................................

..................................................

*You shall have a fishy*
*On a little dishy,*
*You shall have a fishy*
*When the boat comes in.*

Baby in the bath

# Going Out

First playgroup

..........................................

..........................................

..........................................

First time baby fed the ducks

..........................................

..........................................

..........................................

First visit to the playground

..........................................

..........................................

..........................................

First time on a merry-go-round

..........................................

..........................................

..........................................

First visit to the zoo

..........................................

..........................................

..........................................

Family weekend activities

..........................................

..........................................

..........................................

## Going Out to:

The swimming pool

..........................................

..........................................

..........................................

Cafes and restaurants

..........................................

..........................................

..........................................

The shops

..........................................

..........................................

..........................................

Parks and gardens

..........................................

..........................................

..........................................

The beach

..........................................

..........................................

..........................................

The countryside

..........................................

..........................................

..........................................

Bus

...........................................................
...........................................................
...........................................................
...........................................................

*Visiting*
Grandparents

...........................................................
...........................................................
...........................................................

Relatives

...........................................................
...........................................................

Friends

...........................................................
...........................................................
...........................................................

*Trips by:*
Pram/stroller

...........................................................
...........................................................
...........................................................
...........................................................
...........................................................

Car

...........................................................
...........................................................

Train

...........................................................
...........................................................
...........................................................
...........................................................

Plane

...........................................................
...........................................................

Other

...........................................................
...........................................................
...........................................................

# Clever Girl

First waved goodbye

..............................................

..............................................

First played peek-a-boo

..............................................

..............................................

First clapped hands

..............................................

..............................................

First pulled a pull-along toy

..............................................

..............................................

First picked up tiny objects

..............................................

..............................................

First stacked blocks

..............................................

..............................................

First turned the pages of a book

..............................................

..............................................

First joined in singing a song

..............................................

..............................................

First put on their own clothes

..............................................

..............................................

First danced

..............................................

..............................................

Other baby firsts

..............................................

..............................................

..............................................

..............................................

..............................................

..............................................

..............................................

..............................................

..............................................

..............................................

One, two,
Buckle my shoe.
Three, four,
Knock on the door.
Five, six,
Pick up sticks.
Seven, eight,
Lay them straight.
Nine, ten,
Big fat hen!

Clever baby girl

Round and round the garden,
Like a teddy bear.
One step, two steps,
Tickle you under there!

# Healthy Girl

## Vaccinations

| Age | Vaccinations | Date Given* |
|---|---|---|
| Birth | Hepatitis B | |
| 2 months | Diptheria/Tetanus/Pertussis<br>Oral Polio Vaccine<br>Hepatitis B<br>H. Influenzae Type b | |
| 4 months | Diptheria/Tetanus/Pertussis<br>Oral Polio Vaccine<br>Hepatitis B<br>H. Influenzae Type b | |
| 6 months | Diptheria/Tetanus/Pertussis<br>Oral Polio Vaccine | |
| 12 months | Measles/Mumps/Rubella<br>Hepatitis B<br>H. Influenzae Type b | |

Other Vaccinations

| Age | Vaccinations | Date Given |
|---|---|---|
| | | |
| | | |
| | | |
| | | |
| | | |

Any reactions

........................................................

........................................................

........................................................

........................................................

........................................................

*Note – vaccination schedules may vary. The above is a guide only.

# Health and Development Checks

Health care professionals

...................................................................

...................................................................

...................................................................

...................................................................

...................................................................

Visits to health care professionals

| Age | Date | Comment |
|-----|------|---------|
|     |      |         |
|     |      |         |
|     |      |         |
|     |      |         |
|     |      |         |
|     |      |         |
|     |      |         |
|     |      |         |
|     |      |         |
|     |      |         |
|     |      |         |
|     |      |         |
|     |      |         |
|     |      |         |

Three cheeky monkeys,

Bouncing on the bed,

One fell off and bumped his head.

Mama called the doctor,

And the doctor said;

No more monkeys,

Bouncing on the bed!

# 2 Months Old

Usually woke for the day at

......................................................

......................................................

Went to bed for the day at

......................................................

......................................................

Daytime sleep routine

......................................................

......................................................

......................................................

......................................................

Daytime feeding routine

......................................................

......................................................

......................................................

Night-time sleeping
and feeding routine

......................................................

......................................................

......................................................

Weight

......................................................

Length

......................................................

Head circumference

......................................................

Crying periods

......................................................

......................................................

......................................................

......................................................

Best way to calm your baby girl

......................................................

......................................................

......................................................

......................................................

......................................................

Changes

......................................................

......................................................

......................................................

New sounds

......................................................

......................................................

......................................................

......................................................

New firsts

..............................................

..............................................

..............................................

..............................................

..............................................

Your baby girl's temperament

..............................................

..............................................

..............................................

..............................................

Nicknames

..............................................

..............................................

..............................................

..............................................

Description of a typical day

..............................................

..............................................

..............................................

..............................................

..............................................

Baby at 2 months

Photo caption

..............................................

..............................................

..............................................

Date photo taken

..............................................

..............................................

# 4 Months Old

Baby at 4 months

Photo caption

......................................................

......................................................

......................................................

Date photo taken

......................................................

Night-time sleeping
and feeding routine

......................................................

......................................................

......................................................

Usually woke for the day at

......................................................

......................................................

Went to bed for the day at

......................................................

......................................................

Daytime sleep routine

......................................................

......................................................

Daytime feeding routine

......................................................

Weight

......................................................

Length

......................................................

Head circumference

......................................................

Time spent playing on the floor

.................................................

.................................................

.................................................

.................................................

Crying periods

.................................................

.................................................

.................................................

Best way to calm your baby girl

.................................................

.................................................

.................................................

Changes

.................................................

.................................................

.................................................

New sounds

.................................................

.................................................

.................................................

New firsts

.................................................

.................................................

.................................................

Your baby girl's temperament

.................................................

.................................................

.................................................

Nicknames

.................................................

.................................................

.................................................

Description of a typical day

.................................................

.................................................

.................................................

Preferred activities

.................................................

.................................................

.................................................

Preferred foods

.................................................

.................................................

.................................................

.................................................

# 6 Months Old

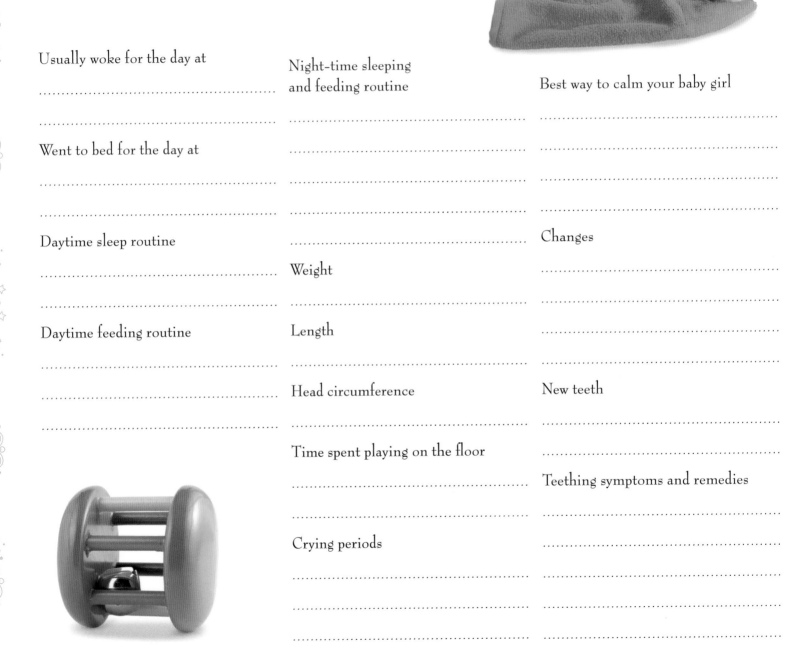

Usually woke for the day at

..............................................

Went to bed for the day at

..............................................

..............................................

Daytime sleep routine

..............................................

..............................................

Daytime feeding routine

..............................................

..............................................

Night-time sleeping
and feeding routine

..............................................

..............................................

..............................................

..............................................

Weight

..............................................

Length

..............................................

Head circumference

..............................................

Time spent playing on the floor

..............................................

..............................................

Crying periods

..............................................

..............................................

..............................................

Best way to calm your baby girl

..............................................

..............................................

..............................................

Changes

..............................................

..............................................

..............................................

New teeth

..............................................

..............................................

Teething symptoms and remedies

..............................................

..............................................

..............................................

Baby at 6 months

New sounds

......................................................

......................................................

New firsts

......................................................

......................................................

......................................................

......................................................

Your baby girl's temperament

......................................................

......................................................

......................................................

Nicknames

......................................................

......................................................

Description of a typical day

......................................................

......................................................

Preferred activities

......................................................

......................................................

......................................................

Photo caption

......................................................

......................................................

......................................................

......................................................

Date photo taken

......................................................

Preferred foods

......................................................

......................................................

......................................................

33

# 8 Months Old

Usually woke for the day at

......................................................

......................................................

Went to bed for the day at

......................................................

......................................................

Daytime sleep routine

......................................................

......................................................

Daytime feeding routine

......................................................

......................................................

Night-time sleeping
and feeding routine

......................................................

......................................................

......................................................

Photo caption

......................................................

......................................................

......................................................

......................................................

Date photo taken

......................................................

......................................................

Baby at 8 months

Weight

..................................................

Length

..................................................

Head circumference

..................................................

Time spent playing on the floor

..................................................

..................................................

Crying periods

..................................................

..................................................

Best way to calm your baby girl

..................................................

..................................................

..................................................

Changes

..................................................

..................................................

..................................................

New teeth

..................................................

..................................................

..................................................

Teething symptoms and remedies

..................................................

..................................................

..................................................

New sounds

..................................................

..................................................

New firsts

..................................................

..................................................

Your baby girl's temperament

..................................................

..................................................

Nicknames

Description of a typical day

..................................................

..................................................

..................................................

..................................................

Preferred activities

..................................................

..................................................

..................................................

Preferred foods

..................................................

..................................................

..................................................

# 10 Months Old

Usually woke for the day at

..................................................

..................................................

Went to bed for the day at

..................................................

..................................................

Daytime sleep routine

..................................................

..................................................

Daytime feeding routine

..................................................

..................................................

Night-time sleeping
and feeding routine

..................................................

..................................................

..................................................

..................................................

Weight

..................................................

Length

..................................................

Head circumference

..................................................

Time spent playing on the floor

..................................................

..................................................

Crying periods

..................................................

..................................................

..................................................

Best way to calm your baby girl

..................................................

..................................................

..................................................

Changes

..................................................

..................................................

..................................................

New teeth

..................................................

..................................................

Teething symptoms and remedies

..................................................

..................................................

..................................................

Baby at 10 months

New sounds

......................................................

......................................................

New firsts

......................................................

......................................................

......................................................

Your baby girl's temperament

......................................................

......................................................

......................................................

Nicknames

......................................................

......................................................

Description of a typical day

......................................................

......................................................

Preferred activities

......................................................

......................................................

......................................................

Photo caption

......................................................

......................................................

......................................................

Date photo taken

......................................................

Preferred foods

......................................................

......................................................

......................................................

# 12 Months Old

Usually woke for the day at

.......................................

.......................................

Went to bed for the day at

.......................................

.......................................

Daytime sleep routine

.......................................

.......................................

Daytime feeding routine

.......................................

.......................................

Night-time sleeping
and feeding routine

.......................................

.......................................

.......................................

Baby at 12 months

Photo caption

.......................................

.......................................

.......................................

.......................................

Date photo taken

.......................................

.......................................

Weight

.......................................................

Length

.......................................................

Head circumference

.......................................................

Time spent playing on the floor

.......................................................

.......................................................

Crying periods

.......................................................

.......................................................

Best way to calm your baby girl

.......................................................

.......................................................

.......................................................

Changes

.......................................................

.......................................................

.......................................................

New teeth

.......................................................

.......................................................

.......................................................

Teething symptoms and remedies

.......................................................

.......................................................

.......................................................

.......................................................

New sounds

.......................................................

.......................................................

New firsts

.......................................................

.......................................................

.......................................................

Your baby girl's temperament

.......................................................

Nicknames

.......................................................

.......................................................

Description of a typical day

.......................................................

.......................................................

.......................................................

Preferred activities

.......................................................

.......................................................

.......................................................

.......................................................

Preferred foods

.......................................................

.......................................................

.......................................................

# Your Baby Girl's Firsts

First smile

..................................................

..................................................

First gripped rattle

..................................................

..................................................

First laughed

..................................................

..................................................

First tooth

..................................................

..................................................

First haircut

..................................................

..................................................

Clever baby girl

First slept through the night

..................................................

..................................................

First said 'Mama'

..................................................

..................................................

Photo caption

..................................................

..................................................

..................................................

Date photo taken

..................................................

First said 'Dada'

......................................

......................................

First waved goodbye

......................................

......................................

First rolled

......................................

......................................

First sat

......................................

......................................

First crawled

......................................

......................................

First stood

......................................

......................................

First walked

......................................

......................................

First babysitter

......................................

*I had a little nut tree,*
*Nothing would it bear,*
*But a silver nutmeg,*
*And a golden pear.*

# First Christmas

## Christmas Eve

**Where the day was spent**

.................................................
.................................................
.................................................
.................................................
.................................................

**Who was there**

.................................................
.................................................
.................................................
.................................................

**Baby's outfit**

.................................................
.................................................

**Description of your baby girl's first Christmas Eve**

.................................................
.................................................
.................................................

## Christmas Day

**Where the day was spent**

.................................................
.................................................
.................................................
.................................................
.................................................

**Who was there**

.................................................
.................................................
.................................................
.................................................

**Your present to your baby girl**

.................................................
.................................................
.................................................
.................................................
.................................................

**Other presents**

.................................................
.................................................
.................................................
.................................................

Present your baby girl loved the most

..............................................................

..............................................................

First Christmas meal

..............................................................

..............................................................

..............................................................

Baby girl's outfit

..............................................................

..............................................................

..............................................................

Description of the Christmas tree

..............................................................

..............................................................

..............................................................

Description of your baby girl's first
Christmas Day

..............................................................

..............................................................

..............................................................

..............................................................

*On the first day of Christmas
My true love gave to me
A partridge in a pear tree.*

First Christmas

Photo caption

..............................................................

..............................................................

Date photo taken

..............................................................

..............................................................

# First Birthday

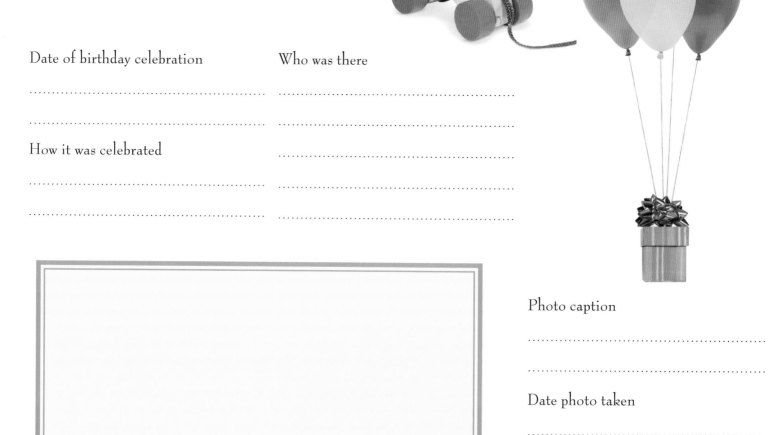

Date of birthday celebration

.................................................................

.................................................................

How it was celebrated

.................................................................

.................................................................

Who was there

.................................................................

.................................................................

.................................................................

.................................................................

Photo caption

.................................................................

.................................................................

Date photo taken

.................................................................

Your present to your baby girl

.................................................................

.................................................................

.................................................................

.................................................................

First birthday

44

Other presents

.....................................................

.....................................................

.....................................................

.....................................................

.....................................................

Baby girl's outfit

.....................................................

.....................................................

How baby behaved

.....................................................

.....................................................

.....................................................

Baby girl's reaction when
'Happy Birthday' sung

.....................................................

.....................................................

.....................................................

.....................................................

.....................................................

Description of cake

.....................................................

.....................................................

.....................................................

Description of birthday celebration

.....................................................

.....................................................

.....................................................

.....................................................

.....................................................

.....................................................

Memorable moments

.....................................................

.....................................................

.....................................................

.....................................................

.....................................................

.....................................................

.....................................................

.....................................................

.....................................................

# Going on Holiday

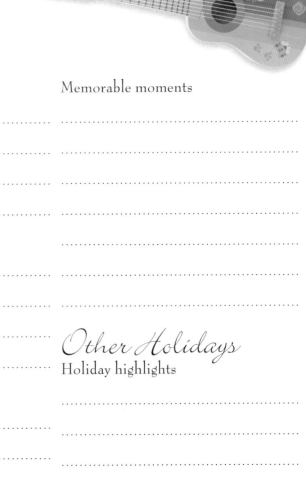

### First Holiday

People who went

........................................
........................................
........................................
........................................

How long away

........................................
........................................
........................................

Getting there details

........................................
........................................
........................................

Accommodation details

........................................
........................................
........................................

Toys and books taken

........................................
........................................
........................................

Baby girl's holiday routine

........................................
........................................
........................................

New experiences

........................................
........................................
........................................

Holiday highlights

........................................

Memorable moments

........................................
........................................
........................................
........................................

### Other Holidays

Holiday highlights

........................................
........................................
........................................

Memorable moments

........................................
........................................
........................................

On holiday

Photo caption

...............................................................

...............................................................

Date photo taken

...............................................................

Mary had a little lamb,
Its fleece was white as snow;
And everywhere that Mary went
The lamb was sure to go.

# Looking Back

## Baby Girl's First Year

Greatest pleasure

.........................................................................
.........................................................................
.........................................................................
.........................................................................
.........................................................................
.........................................................................
.........................................................................

Greatest challenge

.........................................................................
.........................................................................
.........................................................................
.........................................................................
.........................................................................
.........................................................................
.........................................................................
.........................................................................

Siblings' early reaction to baby

.........................................................................
.........................................................................
.........................................................................
.........................................................................
.........................................................................
.........................................................................

Siblings' relationship
with baby now

.........................................................................
.........................................................................
.........................................................................
.........................................................................
.........................................................................
.........................................................................

Your baby girl's personality

.........................................................................
.........................................................................
.........................................................................
.........................................................................
.........................................................................
.........................................................................

Thoughts on being a family

.........................................................................
.........................................................................
.........................................................................
.........................................................................
.........................................................................